The Magic Sch[...]® Builds the Statue of Liberty

SCHOLASTIC INC.
New York Toronto London Auckland Sydney
Mexico City New Delhi Hong Kong Buenos Aires

We have fun in Ms. Frizzle's class.
We go on trips in the Magic School Bus.
TRIP TODAY!
LET'S GO!
THIS TRIP COULD BE FUN.
WELL, ANYTHING IS POSSIBLE.

Today we are going to the Statue of Liberty.
It is on Liberty Island.
The island is in the water near New York City.

We will find out how the statue was made.
Then we will make a little
Statue of Liberty in our classroom.
WHAT IS *LIBERTY*?
WHEN PEOPLE HAVE LIBERTY, IT MEANS THEY ARE FREE.
AM I FREE TO SKIP THIS TRIP?

Now it is time to go.
"Please get on the bus, class,"
says Ms. Frizzle.
What Is a Free Country?
by Wanda
In some countries,
a king tells people what
to do.
In a free country,
people make the rules
together.
VOTE
TODAY!

The Friz drives to the Statue of Liberty.
But on the way,
something funny happens.
We go back in time!
The bus changes. Our clothes change, too.

IT IS MORE THAN 100 YEARS AGO, CHILDREN.
NEW YORK EMPORIUM
LOOK! OUR BUS IS A HORSE AND CARRIAGE.
NOW WE CAN HORSE AROUND!
1870!

When we get to the island,
there is no statue!
"Where is it, Ms. Frizzle?" we ask.
"The statue has not been built yet,"
says our teacher.
THE STATUE OF LIBERTY WAS MADE IN FRANCE.
FRANCE IS FAR AWAY.
USA
FRANCE
The Statue Was a Gift from France
by Phoebe
America is a free country. The French people gave the statue to America to show that they love freedom, too.
The base of the statue was made in America.

The bus becomes a ship.
We sail to France.
I FEEL SEA BREEZES.
I FEEL SEASICK.

We arrive in Paris.
Paris is a beautiful city in France.
HOTEL
CAN WE STOP FOR FRENCH FRIES?
YUM! OR FRENCH TOAST!

We see a man with a model of the statue. "Class, this is Frederic-Auguste Bartholdi," says the Friz. "He is the man who will build the statue."
HOW TO SAY HIS NAME: Bar-TOLD-ee
I'M READY TO START WORKING!
WE'LL HELP YOU!

Bartholdi's workshop is big.
But the statue will be bigger.
It will be too big to fit inside.
Bartholdi will make it in pieces.
THE FINISHED STATUE WILL LOOK JUST LIKE THIS MODEL.
BUT IT WILL BE MUCH, MUCH BIGGER!

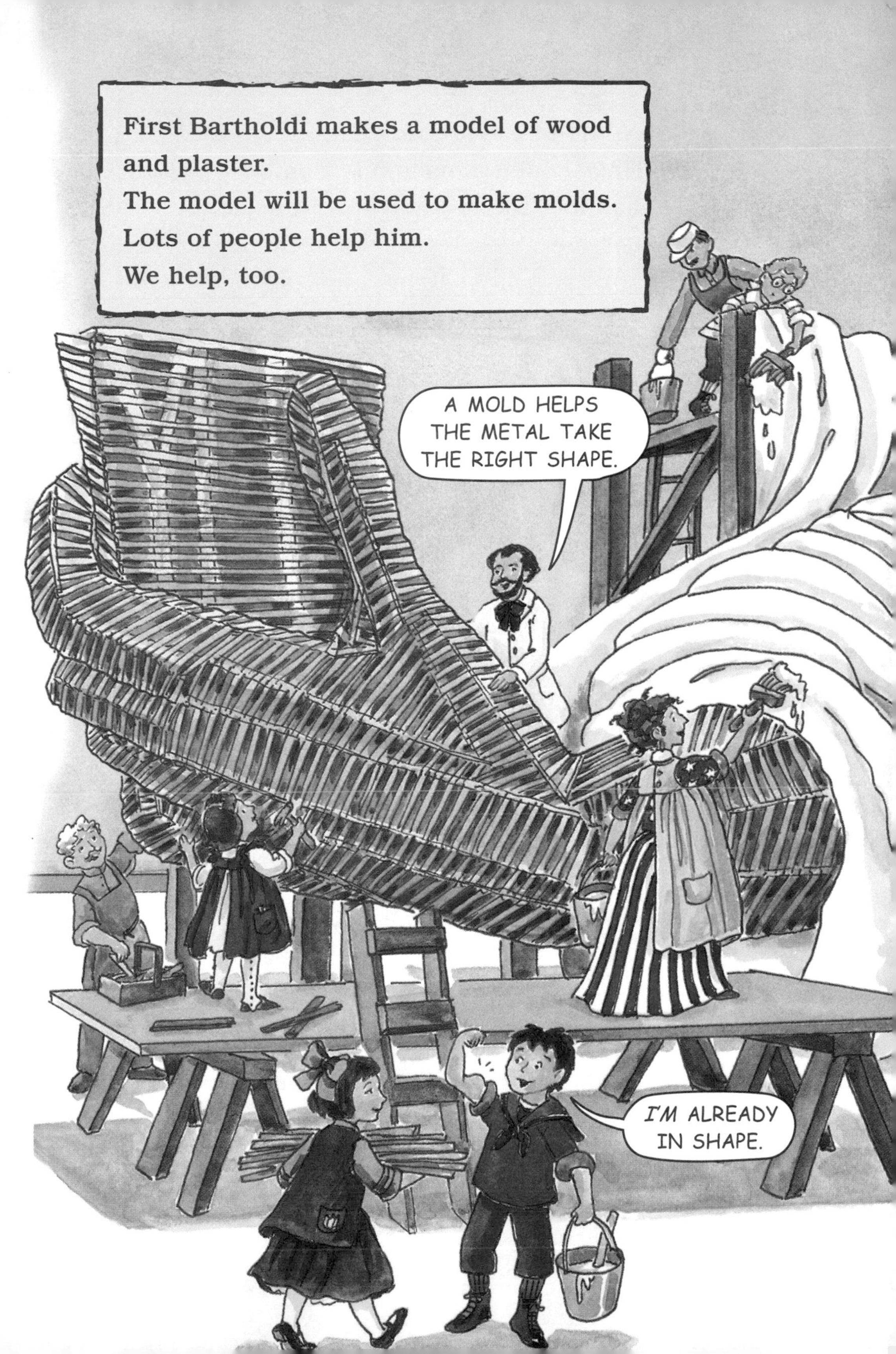
First Bartholdi makes a model of wood and plaster.
The model will be used to make molds.
Lots of people help him.
We help, too.
A MOLD HELPS THE METAL TAKE THE RIGHT SHAPE.
I'M ALREADY IN SHAPE.

PRIVÉ
When the molds are ready,
we place copper sheets on them.
We hammer the copper into the molds.
THAT'S WHAT I CALL HEAVY METAL.
NOT REALLY. THE PIECES ARE LIGHT ENOUGH TO MOVE BY HAND.

Why Is the Statue of Liberty Made of Copper?
by Ralphie
Copper is light and strong. It is light enough to send across the ocean on a ship. It is strong enough to hold its shape in wind and rain.
THE COPPER IS AS THICK AS A PENNY.

Now we are ready to build the statue.
We put the copper pieces over an iron frame.
The finished statue towers over the city!
I USED TO THINK MY *DAD* WAS TALL. . . .

Now the statue will be shipped to America.
We take the statue apart.
Then we pack the pieces in crates.
Oops! *We* get packed in a crate.
PIED (foot)
TORCHÉ
I DON'T THINK I CAN *FACE* THIS TRIP.
UH OH!
NYC NY USA
STATUE DE LA LIBERTE
VISAGE (face)

The crates go on a ship.
There are newspapers in our crate.
We read some of them.
They tell about the statue!
IT SAYS HERE THAT THE BASE ISN'T READY.
AMERICANS DID NOT GIVE ENOUGH MONEY TO BUILD IT.
NY HARBOR

PARIS TO NYC, NY, USA
LOOK! THE NEWSPAPER WANTS TO RAISE MONEY.
THE PAPER WILL PRINT THE NAME OF EVERYONE WHO SENDS MONEY!

At last, we arrive in America. When the base is ready, workers set up the statue.
THE STATUE LOOKS ORANGE.
IN OUR TIME, SHE IS GREEN.
MAYBE SHE GOT SEASICK, TOO.
NO, ARNOLD, AIR MAKES COPPER TURN GREEN OVER TIME.

Bartholdi hangs a French flag
over the statue's face.
No one will see her
until there is a celebration.
PEOPLE ARE COMING TO WATCH THE FLAG DROP.
THEY CAN WATCH FROM THEIR BOATS.
MAGNOLIA

There is a big party for the statue.
The president of the United States
comes to say thank you.
Bartholdi goes up into the statue.
BARTHOLDI REALLY KNOWS THAT STATUE INSIDE AND OUT!
LET'S GO WITH HIM!

The Magic School Bus gets smaller.
We ride on Mr. Bartholdi's hat.
Up, up, up we go!
THE STATUE IS BREATHTAKING.
SO IS CLIMBING ALL THESE STAIRS!

Bartholdi goes up into the crown.
He pulls a cord and the flag falls away.
Ms. Frizzle hits a button
and the bus flies out of the statue.
THE STATUE LOOKS BEAUTIFUL.
I WISH I GOT GIFTS THAT BIG!
IT'S BIG ENOUGH FOR A WHOLE COUNTRY.

Now, when people come to America by boat, the first thing they see is the Statue of Liberty.

We go back to *our* time.
The bus gets big again.
GOOD-BYE, LADY LIBERTY!
THE WHOLE WORLD KNOWS SHE STANDS FOR AMERICA.
WELL, SHE *HAS* BEEN STANDING THERE A LONG TIME.

Ms. Frizzle drives back to school.
HURRY UP!
WE HAVE WORK TO DO.
SCHOOL SWEET SCHOOL!

In our classroom, we finish our Statue of Liberty.
It is not so big, but it looks great!

DATES FOR THE STATUE OF LIBERTY
YEAR
EVENT
1876
Bartholdi starts building in Paris
1884
Statue completed
1885
Statue shipped to USA
1886
Pedestal completed and Statue is rebuilt
1986
Statue celebrated her 100th Birthday
BILL OF RIGHTS

I WONDER WHERE WE'LL GO NEXT.

FUN FACTS ABOUT THE STATUE OF LIBERTY

- The Statue of Liberty is taller than a 20-story building.
- Her feet are 25 feet long. Her sandals would be a size 879!
- Each of her fingers is longer than a person.
- There are 354 steps leading to the crown.
- The Statue of Liberty weighs about 225 tons. That's as much as 3,000 people!
- The 7 spikes of the crown are for the 7 continents and 7 seas of the world.